DEDICATION

For the Waikīkī Aquarium. Happy 100th Birthday!
Jane Shapiro

To Stephen, Eve and Daisy.
With love, Yuko

Published and distributed by

ISLAND HERITAGE
P U B L I S H I N G

94-411 KŌʻAKI STREET, HONOLULU, HAWAII 96797
ORDERS: (800) 468-2800 • INFORMATION: (808) 564-8800
FAX: (808) 564-8877 • islandheritage.com

ISBN#: 0-89610-768-X
First Edition, First Printing - 2003

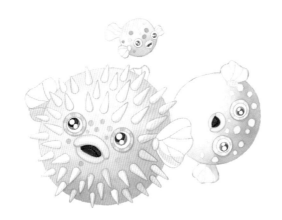

The
BUSY BEACH

Written by Jane H. Shapiro

Illustrated by Yuko Green

ISLAND HERITAGE

On a blue Hawaiian evening,
white waves splash on the beach.

2

3

Ten terns flap and screech above

nine spiny *'ina* nibbling near lava rocks.

A hermit crab slogs her outgrown
shell through the wet sand.

6

A monk seal plunges deep,
looking for a lobster dinner.

7

The beach is busy tonight.

9

An octopus, *he'e*,
wriggles his *eight* arms in
the cool water. *Seven* coconut
palms rattle in the wind. Shiny
naupaka leaves flicker in the dark.

11

The crawling crab searches for a shell that fits.

A tiger shark circles the hungry seal.

The beach is busy tonight.

14

Six sea cucumbers squirt sticky strings.

Five 'o'opu-hue fish puff up like scary balloons.

A kōlea bird patrols a grassy plot.
The hermit crab claws at a broken shell.

The seal flees through the salty sea.

The beach is busy tonight.

20

A yellow-striped *mamo* fish loops above his nest of pink eggs. **Four** red sea stars squiggle over the hard coral.

Three eels slither through the gritty tide.

The crab scrambles into her jagged new home.

The seal flops, famished but safe, on shore.

The beach is busy tonight.

26

A huge turtle, *honu*, paddles past the squishy *limu*.
A darting dragonfly drops onto an *'ohai* bush.
The silver moon rises over the ocean.

Cozy at last, the crab's *two* blue eyes
slide inside her shell.
One seal sniffs, snorts, and snores. Asleep.

The beach is busy, bus-Z-Z-Z-Z-Z-Z-y tonight.

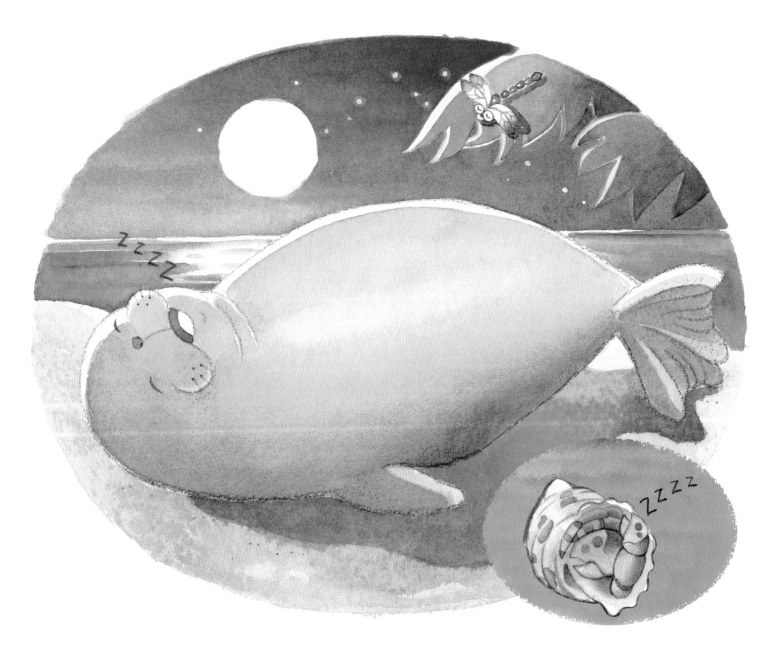

THE END

GLOSSARY
(in order of appearance)

TERNS

There are several kinds of these birds in the islands. Two of the Hawaiian varieties are *noio* and *'eki'eki*.

'INA or
SEA URCHINS

Many species of *'ina* nibble, usually on seaweed, in the Hawaiian waters. Most, like rock-boring urchins, have spines that are sharp. A few have spines that are also venomous and can sting; these are *wana*.

HERMIT CRABS or
PAPA'I IWI PUPU

In other parts of the world you can find hermit crabs that breathe air on land, but in Hawai'i they all get their oxygen from the water. Each hermit crab has a hard skeleton on the outside of most its body. However, to protect its softer abdomen it crawls inside an empty snail shell. As it grows it moves into larger shells.

HAWAIIAN MONK SEALS or
'ILIO-HOLO-I-KAUAUA

This species is found only in Hawai'i (endemic) and is now endangered with just over one thousand remaining. Monk seals dive to great depths to find food, but much of their time they rest on beaches in the remote Northwestern Hawaiian Islands. Tiger sharks are the main predators of monk seals.

LOBSTER

The spiny Hawaiian lobster, *ula*, is blue or red. It's a favorite food of both the monk seal and the octopus.

OCTOPUS

He'e is the name for the Hawaiian octopus. This sea creature has inspired many legends based on its cleverness.

COCONUT PALMS

Called *niu* in Hawaiian, palm trees have many varieties and many uses. They grow along the shore as well as far inland.

BEACH *NAUPAKA* or
NAUPAKA-KAHAKAI

These plants have slick, thick leaves that reflect the sun and store water. *Naupaka* grows well at the beach, which is usually hot and dry. Other species grow high up on mountain slopes.

TIGER SHARK

The waters of Hawai'i have two dozen kinds of sharks, some dangerous and some harmless. All sharks can be called by the same name in Hawaiian, *manō*.

SEA CUCUMBERS or *LOLI*	Sea cucumbers are soft, but protect themselves from predators in many ways. With flexible bodies, they may hide under, or appear as, rocks. Some *loli* also have bad-tasting chemicals in their skin, while others can eject white sticky threads if disturbed.
BALLOON FISH	If threatened, these fish can inflate themselves to look much larger and scare off an enemy.
KŌLEA **or PACIFIC GOLDEN-PLOVER**	Flocks of these birds visit Hawaiʻi from August through April, returning to the same grassy spot each year. This is their territory and they chase off other kōlea who venture too close.
MAMO **or HAWAIIAN SERGEANT DAMSELFISH**	Male *mamo* change the color of their stripes from black to yellow and swim loops above the seafloor to attract female *mamo* to their nests. After the female lays pink-colored eggs, the male guards the eggs and keeps them clean. The *mamo* is endemic to the Hawaiian Islands.
SEA STARS	The general Hawaiian name for starfish is *peʻa*. These slow-moving reef creatures are also found in tide pools, and come in many colors. In Hawaiʻi three of the red variety are the velvet, the toenail and the dwarf sea stars.
EELS	In Hawaiian eels are called *pūhi*. There are many kinds, large and small, and all love to hide in underwater holes.
HONU	Gentle, beloved creatures, turtles can grow to be a yard long and weigh up to four hundred pounds. They are a protected species in Hawaiʻi.
LIMU	This is the general Hawaiian term for hundreds of kinds of seaweed, food for many sea creatures and people, too.
PINAO	Hawaiian dragonflies are called *pinao*. They can be seen everywhere in the islands, all the way from the beach up into the mountains.
ʻOHAI	This endangered beach plant is found only in Hawaiʻi. It still grows at Kaʻena Point on the island of Oʻahu and can also be found on the grounds of the Waikīkī Aquarium.

(All information in THE BUSY BEACH is from materials provided by the education staff at the Waikīkī Aquarium. However, the story is fiction and is the sole responsibility of the author.)

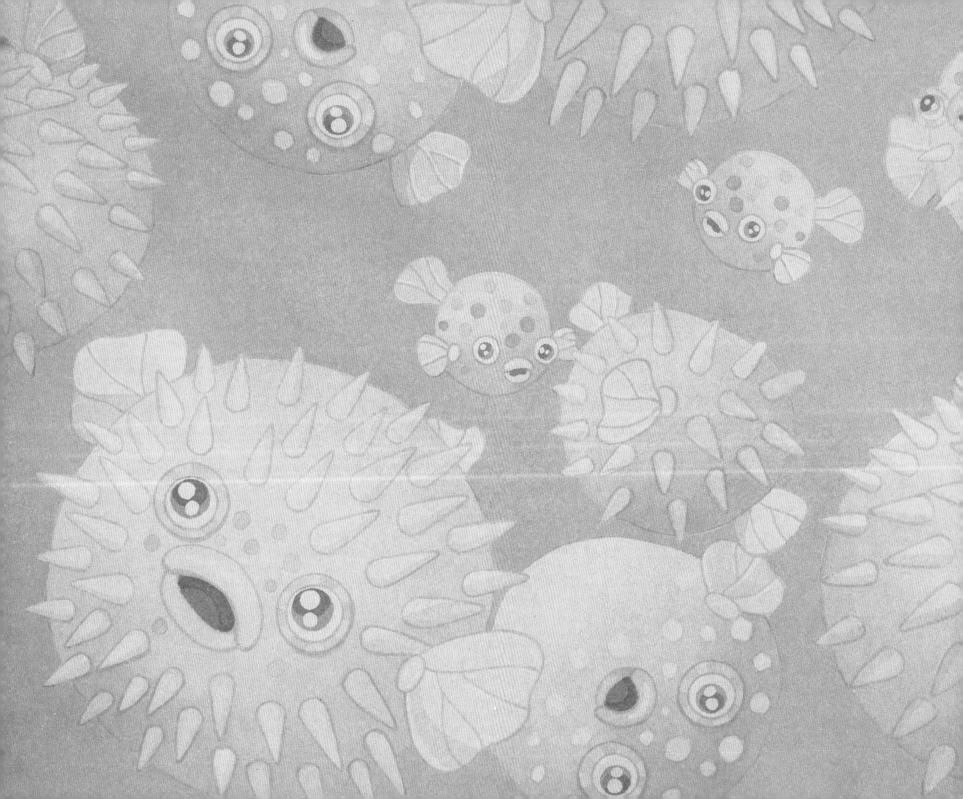